The Way to Go

A Book about Character and Kids Like You!

Acknowledgements

Text John Sydney Tighe

Illustrations Christopher J. Pelicano

Production John Addy

Layout Design Christopher J. Pelicano

Editorial Consultant

Heather M. DuBois, M.Ed

This volume is dedicated to parents, family members, teachers and counselors who work with children everyday to instill in them the basic values that will stay with them throughout their lives. A special thank you goes to Sharen A. Betzold, a committed and talented elementary school teacher for over forty years. Her care and concern for children is at the heart of this volume. *The Way to Go* is also dedicated to the memory of Lewis "Daddy Rew" Holland, whose heart and spirit remained child-like throughout his life. His friendship will be forever cherished.

Thank You!

THE AMBASSADOR
COMPANY
Enriching Your Community

PRINTED AT: Quad/Graphics, Versailles, KY   EDITION 4 : 12/2011

The Way To Go

Sponsored by

Christian Corner Cafe
Dorrece Tanawat
12565 National Road SW
740-927-4414   Etna
www.christiancornercafe.com

The Hair Place
Barbershop
In Business For 28 Years
340 S. Main St.
740-927-8485   Pataskala

ROCHELL
LANDSCAPE & LAWN CARE LLC
34 Front St.
740-927-4600   Pataskala
www.rochellandscape.com

Bright Waters Realty
"Your Hometown Company"
Michele Ball, Broker/Owner
288 S. Main Street
740-927-0767   Pataskala
www.brightwatersrealty.com

BANNER INSURANCE SERVICES
Proudly Representing German Mutual Insurance
399 S. Main Street
740-964-2007   Pataskala
www.bisbestrate.com

Happy Reading!

My Favorite Book is the Way to Go

I want to be friendly
and responsible too
and show good manners
at home and at school.

I want to make good choices
and be caring and good,
to help others in need
like I know I should.

I want to love my family
and community too
and choose everyday
the right things to do.

I want to learn all I can
that will help me to grow.
So this wonderful book
is the best way to go.

My favorite book too
it might just become.
We can read it together
and join in the fun!

Our Great Town

Our town is a great town
where people are helpful and fair;
where people take time with family and friends;
where people really care.

At the pharmacy we ask Miss Lee
about the medicines on our account.
She knows just what the doctor prescribed
and gives us the right amount.

When we moved here Miss Brown led us
to a house just right for us all;
with bushes around the front yard
And a backyard tree that's awesome and tall!

When my brother turned sixteen
Dad said he could get a car,
nothing new... but a good car still
that runs just great so far.

Then Dad said we needed insurance
and we would see Mrs. Sims about that,
just so if anything ever went wrong.
So we sat down with her to chat.

All my teachers work really hard.
They make a great place of our school.
They teach us about the world around us
and following the Golden Rule.

Our class invited a fire fighter
and a police officer to our room.
They talked about recycling and safety
And we asked them to come back soon.

The people at our local bank
are friendly all the time.
I have an account for birthday money
and Mom says it really is mine!

I'll give some to the homeless shelter
And try to save the rest.
The folks at the bank are good to us
They always do their best.

Last Saturday we went shopping
to a crowded but friendly store
to get all kinds of things for our house
and an American flag for over our door.

Then we stopped to eat lunch
But Dad said he would eat light
So he had a salad and said we should too
But we're not on his diet!

On weekends we play sports
like soccer and basketball
in a park that was built with donations
from townspeople one and all.

Our family is busy much of the time
but we try sitting together to eat.
Dinnertime is a great time to talk
Even Coco our lab has a seat!

We live in a really great town
With people who care so much
And so many show it night and day
We call it the "personal touch!"

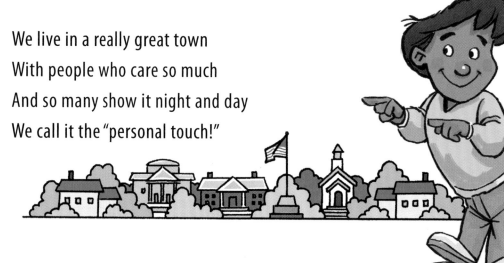

Luis looked up to his big brother, Bobby.

Luis looked up to his big brother, Bobby. Bobby made good grades and was one of the best soccer players on the high school team. Luis knew that Bobby had a lot of friends, and he wanted to have a lot of friends too.

One day Luis was on his way home from school and walking by City Park when he saw Bobby and one of his friends. When Luis looked over at his brother, he saw something that he could not believe. He saw his brother smoking a cigarette while he was talking to his friend.

Luis knew many kids who smoked. Most of them were older, but he even knew kids his own age who had smoked cigarettes. He also knew kids who had smoked marijuana, and he knew that many teenagers and even some younger kids drank beer. Bobby had always seemed so different from those kids. Luis even remembered a time when Bobby came home late from a school dance. He had walked all the way home and explained to their parents that the friend who drove him to the dance had been drinking and that he had refused to get back in the car with him. Several years ago, Luis and Bobby's Uncle Eddie was killed by a driver that had been drinking. Luis remembered that his father was very sad for a very long time.

He remembered too a couple of years ago when his father decided to stop smoking cigarettes, and how happy that had made their mother and the whole family! Luis was thinking of all these things all at the same time because it confused him to see his brother smoking. He had learned in class about the dangers of different kinds of drugs like alcohol, marijuana, tobacco, and many others. So seeing Bobby with a cigarette in his mouth surprised Luis. He just didn't know what to do.

What Should Luis Do?

Here are some of his choices:

Go talk to his counselor at school about how it made him feel to see Bobby smoking, and what could be done about it.

Try smoking a cigarette just to see what was so cool about it.

Go home and tell his parents about seeing Bobby.

Get with Bobby and ask why he is smoking now.

Talk the situation out with some of his friends and see what they think.

Just try to forget about it, and hope that Bobby will stop before he goes on to other kinds of drugs or before he hurts his body too badly.

Choices

What choices could Luis make that would not really help matters at all?

What choices could Luis make that might help?

What would you do if you were in Luis's situation?

Luis didn't get much sleep that night thinking about the situation, and the next morning felt as confused as ever. Back at school, he talked to his friend, Joe.

"Joe," said Luis, "I never thought I would see Bobby smoking! I don't know what to do!"

"Yeah, I know how you feel," said Joe. "My sister got caught drinking last year. I knew about it, but I was afraid to tell anybody."

"You mean you knew she was drinking before she got caught?"

"Yeah, but now I wish I had told some grown up about it. It might have helped her sooner."

"That's what I'm going to do. I am going to tell Miss Patton. She's a counselor, maybe she can help."

So after he talked to Joe, Luis went to Miss Patton, the school counselor. Miss Patton listened to Luis and understood how he felt about Bobby's smoking. She knew he was really disappointed in Bobby's choice. She talked to him about his feelings and some ways to get Bobby to see how he felt. One solution she discussed was telling either Bobby or his parents what he saw. Somehow, Bobby needed to know how disappointed and hurt Luis was and how much he looked up to Bobby. Though Luis did not want to get Bobby in trouble, he knew his parents should know what was going on, even if Bobby was just experimenting. There would be time later for Luis and Bobby to talk alone. Luis thanked Miss Patton and headed home nervously to talk to his parents.

Though it was not the only way to go, Luis thought he had a pretty good plan. And even though he still felt sad about Bobby smoking, now he didn't feel so confused. He knew it was wrong. He knew he couldn't just forget about it, and he knew he didn't need to smoke a cigarette to see what was so cool! Talking to the right people is always a good choice!

Mr. and Mrs. Jackson just bought one of the nicest televisions in the store.

It had the largest screen, the clearest picture, the most bells and whistles and the best sound of any TV they had ever had! Jimmy and Cathy loved it and when their dad brought it home, he complimented Mrs. Jackson on her choice. Mr. Jackson had just picked it up, but it was Mrs. Jackson who had picked it out. Jimmy and Cathy's mom also had a secret plan concerning the new TV that she had not revealed to anyone yet. Of course she and Mr. Jackson would talk about it first but it was going to mean quite a change in their family life.

The secret idea came to her one Saturday when she was carrying in groceries from the car. Mr. Jackson was in the back yard cutting the grass and Jimmy and Cathy were glued to the TV as usual, Jimmy sprawled on the floor and Cathy on the family room sofa. No one thought to say, "Hi, Mom" or "Can I help you with the groceries?" As a matter of fact no one even moved; it was as if they were in a trance. Their mom said, "Hi guys!" as she walked through the room. No response. "Guys?" she said again, waiting for her Jimmy and Cathy to answer.

"Hey you, my beautiful offspring! Are you still alive?" "Oh. Hi, Mom," said Cathy. "Did you say something, Mom?" chimed in Jimmy. "Why, no," said Mrs. Jackson. "I just mentioned that a tornado had taken the roof off our house and your father and I are moving to Hawaii without you, that's all." "Oh, O.K.," said Jimmy, oblivious.

Mrs. Jackson had run into this behavior before. If a TV show they liked was on, the kids paid no attention to anything else: their parents, their manners, nothing! And then when the show was over, all the kids could talk about was how old their TV was. They had been begging for a new one. Mr. Jackson had also mentioned that it was time for a new set. He had said that sometimes he couldn't tell one football team from the other the color was so bad!

Finally, one night after the kids were in bed, their mom asked their dad if he thought the kids watched too much TV. When he replied that he thought they did, indeed watch too much, she said, "Well, what about us?"

"What do you mean 'What about us'?"

"I mean do you think we watch too much TV?"

The question really made Mr. Jackson think. Did he watch too much? He thought of the Sunday afternoons when the kids wanted to go somewhere but he was too absorbed in the football games. He thought of the times that Jimmy and Cathy ate supper without him because he was watching a particular news program. Then Mrs. Jackson chimed in, "You know, Tom, I think about the times late at night when we're so tired but we turn the TV on just to fall asleep. Some of those times it stays on all night."

"You're right," he said. "I guess we do watch a lot of TV. Maybe we ought to cut down."

"Well", said his conscientious wife, "It just so happens that I've been thinking about this."

"Uh oh, you've come up with a plan already, haven't you?"

"I sure have!" said Mrs. Jackson. "Honey, you and I have to sit down together and come up with a TV Plan. We have to do a better job of monitoring what the kids see and how much time we all spend in front of the TV."

"That makes sense", said Mr. Jackson.

"But we need to make this a positive action rather than just taking something away from them."

"Yeah, I thought at the time of our wedding I was getting a pretty smart wife", snickered Mr. Jackson.

"Of course, my dear," she returned playfully. "So, why not have a **Family Night**, where we call in a pizza, talk about the week's activities, maybe play a board game together, or better yet, sometimes we'll read a book together? What do you think?"

"Hey, there's a new set of science fiction books where a group of kids explore outer space together. We could read those!" said Mr. Jackson. Obviously, the idea seemed exciting to him.

When Mr. and Mrs. Jackson sat down to come up with a schedule, they realized that it wasn't just the television that had become too prominent in their home. When the kids weren't in front of the TV, it seemed they were on the computer going to sites where they could talk to their friends or playing computer games. They were listening to music with earphones or talking and texting on cell phones. Mr. and Mrs. Jackson found that new technology meant finding new ways to ensure everyone's safety and to find time together as a family. Phones are great for communicating and computers are great for helping with homework and staying in touch with friends. Television is great for entertainment and learning, at times. But it was time now for the Jackson's to put a little togetherness back in their family life.

So Mr. and Mrs. Jackson laid out the new schedule to Cathy and Jimmy. At first they didn't like so much of their free time being directed in another way. But as time went on they actually began to look forward to **Family Night** and though it was a struggle, they spent a little less time in front of the TV and on the computer or cell phones, and more time talking with the people that love them best, and that they love best... their own family!

Homework

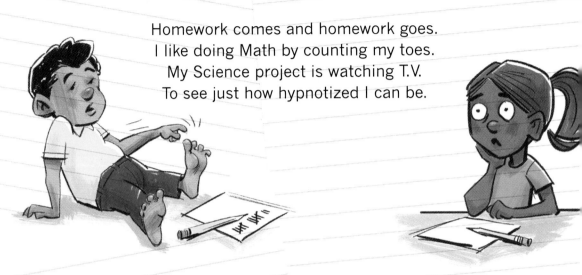

Homework comes and homework goes.
I like doing Math by counting my toes.
My Science project is watching T.V.
To see just how hypnotized I can be.

In Reading my teachers will soon discover
I don't even read comic books cover to cover!
Spelling is all about syllables and sound.
In the Bee I stand... then sit right back down!

Music is my best subject by far.
I turn up the radio and sing in the car.
In P.E. I jump and run and roll,
but too much exercise can take its toll!

So at home I sit, a potato on the couch,
and if I don't get my way I become a grouch.
I've become quite lazy, if you must know.
Even friends say this isn't the way to go.

Can you in these rhyming lines
see yourself at certain times?
Then come a little closer and lend me your ear.
Now that I'm grounded for what seems like a year!

Because I wasn't responsible and didn't do things rightly,
I got talked to and lectured at almost nightly.
So to give teachers and parents (and yourself) some peace,
do your homework each night or your woes will increase!

Question:
What's a woe anyway?

Answer:
Look it up!

Two-thirty was a great time of day.

It meant that school was out. Soon Jeremy would be putting away his backpack and jumping on his bicycle. Jeremy had many friends his age in the neighborhood. There was Jonathan, Tim, Wendi, Eric and Tonya. They had fun hanging out together, playing basketball, and riding their bikes.

Jeremy had one other really good friend, however, who lived across the street from him. He had been his special buddy for as long as he could remember. Jeremy was two and Mr. Horn seventy-five when they first met. Now Jeremy was ten, and his friend was eighty-three. Jeremy had always called his friend "Uncle Cap" because Mr. Horn had been a captain in the army a long time ago and Jeremy's mom said he had to put "Uncle" before it, not because Mr. Horn was really his uncle but because he was "like family", she said, and "Uncle" was a term of respect.

When their friendship began, Jeremy stood about three feet tall, and Uncle Cap, six feet. Many times Uncle Cap would get on his knees so they could look each other eye-to-eye. When Uncle Cap would call for Jeremy he would yell out, "Je-re-miah!" in such a way that he sounded like his name, like a loud, large horn! His voice was deep and hoarse and when he heard it, it always made Jeremy feel warm inside. As Jeremy got older, some days they would just walk and talk and look at the new flowers blooming in Uncle Cap's garden or watch the hummingbirds hover around his red feeder. Sometimes Uncle Cap would tell Jeremy stories from when he went to France in World War II. Mr. Horn was wounded in the war and was sent home to a hospital, where he stayed for many weeks. Outside his window in the hospital were bright flowers and a humming bird feeder. He always said those humming birds helped him make it through hard times.

Jeremy loved Mr. Horn's stories and through the years Jeremy would come over to show his friend a drawing he had made in school or his picture with the City League soccer team or even a funny shaped rock he had found and Mr. Horn would create a whole story out of whatever object it was. Jeremy always wanted to spend time with his old friend and today was no different. After school he rushed over to the Horn's. He had to tell Uncle Cap about the points he had scored in the relay in Physical Education class today. Uncle Cap would be proud of him and turn it into a great story!

But Uncle Cap was not home. Mrs. Horn came to the door and told Jeremy that Mr. Horn had become very sick the night

before and had been taken to the hospital. There the doctors and nurses were taking care of him so that he could get better. Mrs. Horn told Jeremy to be sure to come over to see him when he got home.

A week went by and Uncle Cap did not come home. Jeremy's mom told him that Mrs. Horn was spending most of her time at the hospital. Jeremy missed his friend very much. Each day he rushed home to see if the Captain was home from the hospital. One day he saw white flowers on the porch of the Horn's house. He knew that Uncle Cap must be home now! He ran in to tell his mom that Uncle Cap must be home because he had seen flowers on the front porch.

With tears in her eyes, his mother told him that Uncle Cap would not be coming home. She explained that the flowers on the front porch meant that Uncle Cap had died.

Jeremy couldn't believe what his mother was telling him. He knew Uncle Cap was sick, but he never thought he was going to die! He and Uncle Cap never talked about dying; they always talked about living! Jeremy started to feel almost like he did when he fell off the jungle gym and lost his breath. His heart hurt badly when he tried to understand what his life would be like without his friend. His father and mother answered his questions as he asked them, and they seemed to understand what he was feeling.

Jeremy went to Mr. Horn's funeral, and he was not ashamed to cry because losing his close and special friend was hard. As Jeremy got into bed that night, his mom came in to say good night. Jeremy looked up to her and said, "But Mom, Uncle Cap is still my friend and he'll always be my friend!"

"Yes, son, he will. And Mrs. Horn told me that Uncle Cap left some presents for you to remember him by. She gave them to me after the funeral." The first present Uncle Cap left for Jeremy was his red feeder for the hummingbirds. He left a note of instructions on how to attract the birds to the feeder so Jeremy could see the hummingbirds from his own room. The second was a little story Uncle Cap had written for Jeremy a few weeks before. It was called *The Boy and the Fantastic Drawing.* And the third present was in a little box. When Jeremy opened the box there was a medal in it attached to a purple ribbon with white stripes down the side. The medal was a purple heart that had inside of it a dark gold image of George Washington. It is one of the most important medals that can be given to a soldier and Uncle Cap received it while he was in the hospital after he was wounded over sixty

years ago. Jeremy had never received such wonderful gifts and he was beginning to understand that you never lose a special friend like Uncle Cap. Instead, the lives of special people can be written in your heart as long as you remember them. Jeremy remembered Uncle Cap's large hands and deep laugh. He remembered the delight his friend took in small things like Jeremy himself and the events of Jeremy's life. He remembered his stories and the hummingbirds.

And for many nights to come, Jeremy would fall asleep with Uncle Cap's face, his great wide smile and his kind eyes clear as ever in his mind. In that way and in many other ways, Uncle Cap, a very special friend, still lives on in Jeremy's heart.

Glossary

Friendship – A strong, helpful and affectionate connection to another. (See the Rules of Friendship)

Veteran – One who has served in one of the armed services of our country.

The Purple Heart – A medal given a member of the armed services who was wounded either in combat or because of action taken by the opposing forces.

Happy Memories: A Journal Entry

Write down a happy memory you have of a family member, a special friend or a pet you do not see anymore.

_____

_____

_____

_____

_____

_____

_____

_____

_____

_____

_____

_____

_____

Do you know any veterans or people serving in the military now? Have you ever thanked them for serving our country?

When is Veteran's Day and how can you make that day a special day?

7 Rules of Friendship

1. Friends help each other.

2. Friends like to have fun with each other.

3. Sometimes friends get angry with each other but they always make up.

4. Friends tell each other the truth.

5. Making fun of someone is not very friendly!

6. You cannot be a friend and a bully at the same time!

7. Always treat your friends the way you would like to be treated.

Where to Read a Good Book

My mom once said, "Go read a good book..."
So I wondered which way to go.
Now I know I can read anywhere I look
In places familiar or ones I don't know.

I can read in my house and of course at school,
on a baseball field or by the town center pool,
in summer in my grandma's town,
or in winter waiting for the snow to come down.

I can read on a chair, a stool or a couch.
Standing tall or sitting, in a squat or a crouch.
I can read in the middle of the front or back porch
by light bulb or flashlight or lantern or torch.

I can read in the car on a bus or a plane,
on a boulevard, an avenue, a street or a lane.
In the cool of the shade or the heat of the sun
I can read just as well in either one.

There's always a place to read if you look.
But where am I going to find a good book?
I think I might look for a book right away
I want to begin reading a good book today!

Mrs. Hawkins and the Fourth Graders: A Story

Mr. and Mrs. Hawkins ran the Home Center Hardware Store for many years.

Because they had no children, the couple spent most of their time working together in the store. They made it one of the friendliest places in town, a place where people would come on Saturday mornings to find all the little things that were going to be needed for that day's repairs around the house.

Since Mr. Hawkins had passed away last winter, however, Mrs. Hawkins was having a hard time running things. She knew how because over the years she had done everything there was to do in the store; it was just that things were different without her husband. Even with all her friends and regular customers, she still felt lonely. And then came that terrible morning when she arrived at the store to find the large front windows of the store had been spray painted in different colors and the brick facade surrounding the glass had vulgar words painted all over it.

Mrs. Hawkins was heartbroken. It just didn't make sense to her! The police officers who were investigating suggested that it could have been a certain gang of teenagers, because sometimes they wore those same colors, but they just didn't know for sure.

All that night Mrs. Hawkins wondered about the teenagers, about the particular kinds of troubles that would make them want to destroy things. She wondered why there seemed to be so many bullies these days and what makes people want to hurt others. And she wound up doing what she did most every night, in the quiet of her bedroom; she talked to Mr. Hawkins about it.

Now this is where the fourth graders of Belmont Elementary School come into the picture. Mrs. Matthews, their teacher, had a Community Service Class once a month. On that day, students would come with ideas about a project they could do in the community. This year they had already planted flower bulbs at the courthouse, made sandwiches to send to the homeless shelter and paid a visit to a nursing home. And now it was time again. Tommy thought they could do something around the school, like clean up the gym but Alicia said that Mr. Townsend and his son already did that. She suggested doing something at the Rec Center. Carrie said the only thing to do there would be shovel snow. Tommy said, "I'm good with a shovel!" But the group reminded him that it hadn't snowed since last year and there would be nothing to shovel. The class laughed at Tommy because he was always outspoken and quick to take on a job. Mrs. Matthews told the class that it sounded like they wanted to do something out of the ordinary, something very special. Vincent agreed with her and said that it had to be something the whole class could do together.

Then Antawn, the shiest kid in class who never spoke up, began talking like never before! He said that his dad was reading in the newspaper this morning about what happened to Mrs. Hawkins's storefront. He said, "My dad and I go in the hardware store almost every Saturday. My dad really liked Mr. Hawkins, but he died last year. And Mrs. Hawkins is a real nice lady. She really likes it when kids come in the store." Sherry told the class that the store was near the school and that she had been in it with her mom and dad many times. Tommy was ready to go but the others didn't know what a bunch of kids could do to help. Mrs. Matthews asked Antawn if he had any suggestions.

"Well, since Mrs. Hawkins sells paint, we could get paint from her and paint over the brick wall that was messed up." And Tommy added that if everyone chipped in, they could clean all the windows, too!

"Well, should we vote on helping Mrs. Hawkins at the hardware store?" asked Mrs. Matthews.

Everybody voted to try to help Mrs. Hawkins. Since Antawn knew her, he was elected to visit her and explain the class project. Mrs. Hawkins was overwhelmed when Antawn told her they wanted to help. And the next Saturday, the fourth grade community project group showed up at the Home Center Hardware Store, ready to paint and clean up. When some of the parents heard about the project they were so proud of the class that they went with them to help out.

When the day was done, a freshly painted brick facade framed the big glass windows of the hardware store entrance. Every inch of those windows sparkled. Mrs. Hawkins had supplied cookies and juice, but every time she tried to thank the kids, she started crying. When the work was done, Mrs. Hawkins said, "It's not every day an old woman gets to share the friendship of youngsters like you! I will never forget this day!"

The project was such a success that Mrs. Hawkins gave the fourth grade class a very special gift. For all these years Mr. and Mrs. Hawkins had kept the first sign they had ever put up in front of the store. It was a battered, oval wooden sign with flaking, gold lettering that said, *Home Center Hardware: A Friendly Place.* The kids seemed to understand what a special gift it was, and they hung it above the coat rack in their classroom. It proved to be a great conversation piece, and whenever a visitor to their class asked about it, Tommy, Carrie, Alicia, Vincent, Sherry and everybody, even Antawn, couldn't wait to tell the story of *Mrs. Hawkins and the Fourth Graders.*

Looking Inside a Story

Why was the hardware store so special to Antawn?

_____

_____

What kind of person was Mrs. Hawkins?

_____

_____

Why are stories so much fun?

_____

_____

What is the name given to the person who tells the story?

_____

_____

_____

Glossary

Facade – The front of a building, like the one the fourth graders helped to clean up. There is another meaning for the word facade that has to do with being honest – look up this meaning and write it down.

Vulgar – As it is used in this story, "vulgar" refers to words that are offensive. We call them "dirty" or "ugly" words. Vulgar words can hurt people on the inside. We should stay away from vulgar words.

Word Scramble

Unscramble the words below, then unscramble the letters in the circles to find and unscramble the final word. **Good luck!**

d o s m i w

___ ___ ___ ___ ___ ___

h r t u t

___ ___ ___ ___ ___

h e n y t o s

___ ___ ___ ___ ___ ___ ___

s c e t r p e

___ ___ ___ ___ ___ ___ ___

t c i s y n i e r

___ ___ ___ ___ ___ ___ ___ ___ ___

s n e g i d n r a t u d n

___ ___ ___ ___ ___ ___ ___ ___ ___ ___ ___ ___

What you need to be to do a good job.

___ ___ ___ ___ ___ ___ ___ ___ ___ ___ ___

Doing your best is known as ...

the

___ ___ ___ ___

Look in the back of the book for the **answers** to these Word Scrambles.

Dishonesty THE TEST!!

Its a true/false test, so get ready...

1. You bought something that cost 50 cents. You gave the cashier one dollar and he gave you 75 cents back. You figured since it was his mistake he should pay for it and you kept the extra 25 cents. **You were being dishonest.** (**true** or **false**)

2. Your best friend didn't do last night's math homework. Early this morning he asked if he could copy your homework. Because you are best friends you said it would be O.K. this time and you let him copy it. **Your friend was being dishonest by asking.** (**true** or **false**)

You didn't do anything wrong, however, because you had done your own homework. (**true** or **false**)

3. You forgot to feed your dog Molly her supper. It got to be bedtime and you were just too tired and sleepy to go out and feed her. You gave her an extra helping the next morning, though. As long as your parents don't find out, it'll be okay. You've only forgotten a couple of times. **You were honest enough.** (**true** or **false**)

4. You didn't try your best on a school project. **This is not dishonest because the only one you were cheating was yourself.** (**true** or **false**)

5. You were invited to the birthday party of one of your classmates but a good friend of yours in the class was not invited. When she asked where you were going, you said you had to go somewhere with your family. You said this to keep from hurting your friends feelings. **This was dishonest. (true** or **false)**

For the **answers**, go to the last page and turn the book upside down ... but not until you have answered the questions for yourself ... first.

Let's have some Talks

Let's Talk About Family

Where did your family members live 200 years ago?

I met a kid who was part of a Native American tribe!
What is a tribe, anyway, and how does it work?

Why do people have family reunions?

What is a tradition?

How do your family traditions affect your life?

Let's Talk About Friendship

Using the 7 Rules of Friendship, how do you mend
a friendship that has been injured?

How did you meet your closest friends?

Let's Talk About Community

What is a community?

Who are some of the special people that help
your community be a friendly, safe place to live?

What are the things you most like about your community?

What does it mean to be a good citizen?

Write down your Thoughts

Your Thoughts about Family

My family and I have the most fun when ... _____

_____

_____

_____

_____

Your Thoughts about Friendship

My friends have helped me by ... _____

_____

_____

_____

Your Thoughts about Community

My community is a good place to live because ... _____

_____

_____

_____

_____

Making Connections

FAMILY

What is a foundation and how is your family like one?

What does it mean when we call "Family" the foundation of society?

FRIENDSHIP

Name two historical characters that you think would be good friends.

They may have lived hundreds of years apart!

Why do you think they would be friends and what do you think they might talk about?

COMMUNITY

What is the largest community you know of?

What is the smallest community you know of?

How are they alike?

How are you a part of your community?

The Way to Go

Sometimes I think there are too many me's,
too many me's and too many I's,
too much taking the easy way out,
too much mean talk and too many lies!

Too many kids are bullied at school.
Theirs are the hearts we should touch.
There is too much teasing and too many threats
and too much bullying, way too much!

What's the matter with my friends and me?
What is the matter with all of us?
We're not playing fair at recess
and we're picking on kids on the bus!

But then I think about my mom
who gets up early to get me to school,
and Miss Haynes who is a really good teacher
and Coach Carpenter who is unbelievably cool!

They try so hard to do their best
to teach us things that are good,
like being fair in every situation,
and doing the things we should.

Last week I heard about a kid
who collected cans of soup,
then he gave them to Aid in Crisis
to try to help that group!

And you know that lady Miss Forrest,
who Mom says lives all alone?
She sends Get Well cards to people who are sick
and talks to them on the phone.

Those are the kinds of things
I think I would like to do.
I don't think there is much of that around,
not too much we or too much you!

I think I'll try to be a new me.
I'm making myself a promise
to think of others, not myself,
to be helpful, kind and honest.

If you'd like to join me, please feel free.
I'm sure it will help us grow.
We'll try our best to be good to each other.
That for sure, is the way to go!

Family Discussion Worksheet

Hey Adults, let's all sit down and talk a little bit about some things that are important to kids. And let's have some fun doing it! It's the way to go, you know!

Our Great Town Talk about some of the good people that make a positive difference in the life of your community. What can your child do to help the community now?

Luis and His Choices Talk about all the people your child can go to for help. What are the local community resources for drug education?

The Jackson's New TV Talk about good and bad habits. Can you change a bad habit? Name a TV program that does not go along with your values.

Homework! Have a talk about self-discipline. What are some ways you have to discipline yourself in your day-to-day life? Any homework problems in your house? Help set some goals concerning getting homework done on time.

Uncle Cap Lives On What made Jeremy and Uncle Cap's friendship so special? Does anyone in your family have a close friendship like that? Talk about a time you experienced grief over the loss of someone you loved. Share some happy memories of the person you lost. What is so special about serving our country? What does it mean to be a good citizen?

The Rules of Friendship Share with your child what makes close friendships so very special. What is your child's experience with one of the rules of friendship?

Where to Read a Good Book Talk about you and your child's favorite books. Where is the strangest place you have ever found or read a book?

Puzzles What are some other word games you can play with your child? How about board games the family can play together?

Dishonesty Take the test. Sometimes the honest thing to do is not so apparent. Issues with honesty can sometimes be confusing to youngsters, therefore some good general rules to go by are most helpful to them.

Mrs. Hawkins and the Fourth Graders: A Story Why are bullies and street gangs so dangerous? How did the children feel after helping Mrs. Hawkins? Who is your child's favorite character in the story and why?

Let's Talk What did your child write down about families, communities and friendships? Let's talk about it!

Answers to the Word Scramble : turn the book upside down to read them.

wisdom / truth / honesty / respect/sincerity / understanding / TRUSTWORTHY / The Way to Go